This Holiday Annual belongs to

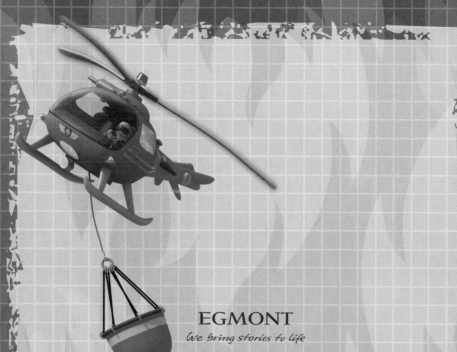

EGMONT
We bring stories to life

First published in Great Britain 2012
by Egmont UK Limited
239 Kensington High Street, London W8 6SA
Edited by Catherine Shoolbred. Designed by Pritty Ramjee.

ISBN 978 1 4052 6275 0

51669/1

Printed in China

What's Inside ...

WELCOME TO PONTYPANDY

Name: Fireman Sam

Job: Firefighter

Likes: Helping people, inventing things and looking after his nephew and niece, James and Sarah

Favourite saying: 'Great Fires of London!'

Drives: Jupiter, Pontypandy's fire engine, and the lifeboat, Neptune

Name: Station Officer Steele

Job: In charge of Pontypandy Fire Station

Likes: Safety checks, rules, training and giving orders

Dislikes: Rule-breakers

Favourite saying: 'Action Stations!'

Name: Elvis Cridlington

Job: Firefighter and fire station cook

Likes: Cooking, singing and looking cool

Favourite instrument: Electric guitar

Favourite saying: 'Great Balls of Fire!'

Name: Penny Morris

Job: Firefighter

Likes: Mechanics, hiking and rock climbing

Favourite saying: 'Go, girl, go!'

Drives: Venus the rescue tender and Neptune the lifeboat

Name: Tom Thomas

Job: Helicopter pilot for Mountain Rescues

Likes: Outdoor sports and rescuing animals in trouble

Favourite saying: 'G'day!'

Drives: The rescue jeep and the rescue helicopter, Wallaby One

The Flood Family

Helen Flood is the local nurse. She drives her white rescue car to help out in emergencies.

Mike Flood is Pontypandy's handyman. He loves playing music with his good friend Elvis.

Mandy Flood is best friends with Norman Price. They love going on adventures together!

The Jones Family

Charlie Jones is Fireman Sam's brother. He is a fisherman and owns a green fishing boat.

Bronwyn Jones works in the fish shop and café. She loves to relax by meditating!

Sarah and James Jones are twins. They enjoy spending time with their Uncle Sam, and playing with Mandy and Norman.

The Price Family

Dilys Price owns the Cut Price Supermarket in Pontypandy. She likes to gossip with her customers over a cup of tea.

Norman Price loves playing tricks and jokes on people. Everyone calls him Naughty Norman because he is always up to something!

Trevor Evans

Trevor Evans is Pontypandy's bus driver. He drives all the children to school and likes to chat to Dilys Price. He loves the great outdoors and is a keen birdwatcher.

SAUSAGES VERSUS PRAWNS

It's the annual sausage **BARBECUE** in Pontypandy. But will everything go to plan?

"We can't wait to try your sausages later!" Dilys tells Trevor.

"How about prawns?" asks Tom. "I'll cook some prawns for you too!"

"Yeah! Then we can see who's the barbecue champ!" says Norman.

Station Office Steele is teaching the team about barbecue safety when he hears a rumbling noise.

"It's Elvis' stomach!" laughs Sam.
"Talking about barbecues is making me HUNGRY!" Elvis smiles.

Trevor sets up his favourite barbecue under a tree. He's also brought an oil drum for rubbish.

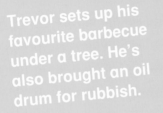

Tom brings his shiny new gas barbecue.

"The food won't taste as good cooked on gas," Trevor tells him. "It will taste **EVEN BETTER!**" Tom replies.

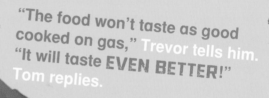

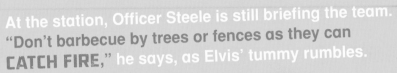

At the station, Officer Steele is still briefing the team. "Don't barbecue by trees or fences as they can **CATCH FIRE**," he says, as Elvis' tummy rumbles.

"And keep gas canisters cool," he adds. "They can **EXPLODE** if they get **TOO HOT!**"

Smoke blows from Trevor's barbecue into Dilys and Norman's eyes.

"You don't have that problem with gas barbecues," smiles Tom. "Mine is SMOKE FREE and ready to cook!"

Soon Tom's barbecued prawns are ready to eat. "**VERY TASTY**," says Dilys.

"Oooh, what's that **DELICIOUS SMELL?!**" asks Norman.

"**BARBECUED SAUSAGES!**" laughs Trevor.

The chefs have a cooking race. Tom turns his gas to full and Trevor pours the rest of the charcoal onto his barbecue.

FLAMES SHOOT UP AND SET FIRE TO THE TREE!

"I'll call **FIREMAN SAM!**" says Bronwyn.

Sam and the fire crew rush to help.

"OH, NO!"

cries Elvis, as he sees that both barbecues have caught fire as well as the tree.

"I don't think we can save the sausages," says Sam, as he pours water on the burning barbecues.

"I hope they have **SOME** food left!" Elvis replies, as his stomach growls again.

Then Elvis spots a gas canister in the fire. He quickly tells Fireman Sam.

"WELL SPOTTED!" Sam replies.

"Keep everyone at a safe distance while Penny and I put out the fire," he adds.

Elvis pumps water so Penny can spray the gas canister to keep it cool, while Sam tackles the rest of the fire.

Before long the fire is out.

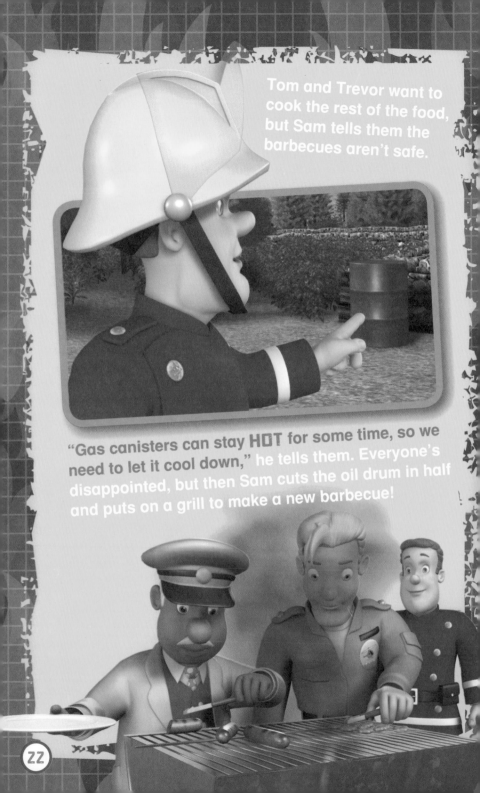

Tom and Trevor want to cook the rest of the food, but Sam tells them the barbecues aren't safe.

"Gas canisters can stay **HOT** for some time, so we need to let it cool down," he tells them. Everyone's disappointed, but then Sam cuts the oil drum in half and puts on a grill to make a new barbecue!

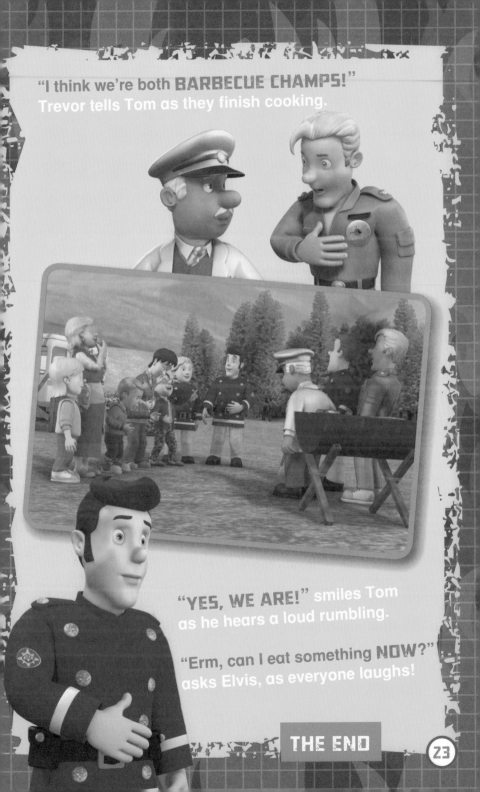

"I think we're both **BARBECUE CHAMPS!**"
Trevor tells Tom as they finish cooking.

"**YES, WE ARE!**" smiles Tom as he hears a loud rumbling.

"Erm, can I eat something **NOW?**" asks Elvis, as everyone laughs!

THE END

23

FIRE SAFETY

Station Officer Steele is giving a fire safety lesson. Talk to a grown-up about how you can stay safe if there is a fire.

1

Keep toys and clothes away from fires and heaters!

2

Don't play near hot cookers or by pans of boiling liquids!

3

If you smell smoke, shout for your family and get help!

4

Leave your house immediately and don't go back inside!

FIRE! FIRE!

There's a fire in Pontypandy. Follow the lines to help Sam and Penny find it, then add a sticker of Jupiter coming to the rescue.

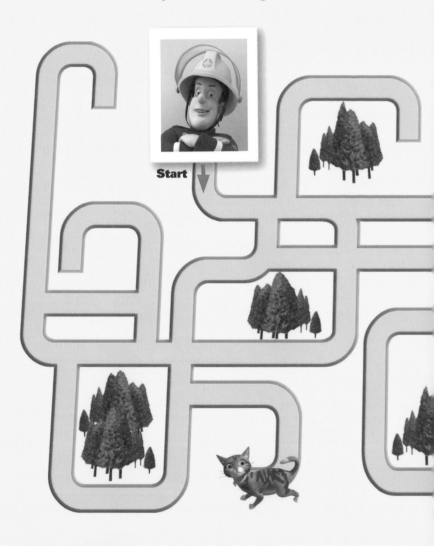

Start

Start

Finish

Finish

Answer on page 60.

WHO'S WHO?

Draw lines to match the descriptions to the right people.

a He's a firefighter who loves to cook!

Norman

b He drives the bus and wears a brown hat.

Elvis

c He has a moustache and runs the fire station.

Trevor

d He wears glasses and is always in trouble.

Officer Steele

Answers on page 60.

MAKING PATTERNS

Add stickers to complete these patterns
of Pontypandy people.

Answers on page 60.

THE COLOUR OF DANGER

Elvis was singing his new song as he cooked lunch in the fire station:

"Red is for danger,
Red is what I said,
So if you're in danger,
The colour is RED!"

Station Officer Steele stormed into the kitchen. "We are not here to sing and dance. We are here to fight fires!" **he said.**

"We certainly are!" said Sam, as he spotted that Elvis' lunch was on FIRE!

Bronwyn was looking after Nipper the dog. He was very excited and raced around the café.

But when Charlie walked in, Nipper ran out of the door and into the road, just missing Nurse Flood's car!

"I'm so sorry, Helen," **Bronwyn said.** "He's my sister's dog and he's full of energy!"

Sam hurried over and handed Nipper to Bronwyn.

SCREEECH!

"You should take him for a long walk to tire him out," **Sam suggested.**

"Good idea, I'll take him along the cliff path," **Bronwyn replied.**

Red is for danger,
Red is what I said,
So if you're in danger,
The colour is **RED**!

At the café, Elvis sang his song while Charlie made some sandwiches to replace his burnt lunch.

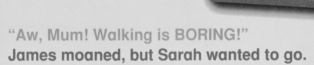

"The twins and I are taking Nipper for a walk," **Bronwyn told Charlie.**

"Aw, Mum! Walking is BORING!" **James moaned, but Sarah wanted to go.**

"You can come fishing with me, James," **said Charlie.** "Don't forget to take your phone!" **he told Bronwyn.**

Later on the cliff path, Sarah and Bronwyn waved at Charlie and James down in their fishing boat.

But while their backs were turned, Nipper got into Bronwyn's bag and took her phone.

"EXCELLENT!" thought Nipper, as he buried it behind a rock.

And when Bronwyn and Sarah ate their lunch, Nipper stole a sandwich!

"NAUGHTY DOG!" shouted Sarah as she chased him along the path.

"AARGH!" Sarah cried, as she fell over and hurt her leg. She quietly sang Elvis' song to make her feel better.

Bronwyn couldn't find her phone, but she saw **SAM** was on the beach, so she jumped up and down and waved at him.

Sam waved back happily. He didn't know that anything was wrong.

"Red is for danger ..." Sarah sang bravely.

"That's it!" said Bronwyn, and she waved their red picnic blanket in the air.

Sam saw her red sign. "Something's wrong!" he said.

He rang Bronwyn's phone, but didn't get an answer.

"I'll get the station to send Tom from Mountain Rescue," he said to himself.

Nipper barked and ran back along the cliff.

"Mum, Nipper's gone!" Sarah shouted.

"I wish we'd never said we'd look after him!" Bronwyn cried.

WOOF!

Suddenly Tom appeared in his HELICOPTER!

He hovered above them, but there was nowhere for him to land.

Nipper ran to the road and **DASHED** in front of Nurse Flood's car again.

She went to grab his collar, but he raced back to the cliff top, so Helen had to follow him.

"What are you doing here?" **Bronwyn asked.**

"Nipper brought me! What's going on?" **Helen replied.**

"Sarah hurt her leg, so Sam climbed up to help us."

Helen thought Sarah's leg needed an **X-RAY** to check if it was broken.

36

Sam called Tom:
"We need to get Sarah to hospital."

"I'll send down a stretcher," Tom replied.

Nurse Helen and Sam lifted Sarah carefully.

"Bye, love!" said Bronwyn. "I'll see you at the hospital."

"Thank goodness for Nipper!" Sam said later, when Sarah was back with her leg in plaster.

"And thanks to Elvis too!" added Sarah. "It's a good job we knew his song …"

RED IS FOR DANGER,
RED IS WHAT I SAID,
SO IF YOU'RE IN DANGER,
THE COLOUR IS RED!

THE END

COUNT UP

How many pictures can you see of Sam, Officer Steele, Jupiter and Tom Thomas? Add stickers of the matching numbers in the boxes below.

Answers on page 60.

WORD SEARCH

Can you find these 5 rescue words in the grid?
Add a trophy sticker when you're found them all.

c	j	s	h	o	s	e
t	n	l	n	k	p	r
t	o	r	c	h	s	e
j	f	t	h	p	b	a
w	k	c	n	o	r	x
n	m	f	r	l	b	e
h	e	l	m	e	t	d

helmet   pole   axe

hose   torch

FIRE STATION FIRE!

Add stickers to complete this picture story about a surprising fire in Pontypandy.

Fireman Sam

Jupiter

Officer Steele

Naughty Norman

Elvis

fire

One morning 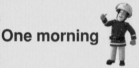 was checking his kit in the fire

station. "It's quiet today so far," said . But then

they received a call out so , Penny and

hurried over to to go to the emergency.

40

Behind the station, was flying paper planes. "The wind slows them down," he said. So he decided to fly his planes inside the fire station instead. walked around the fire station throwing paper planes.

 had left a pot of soup cooking in the kitchen.

didn't see one of his planes land on the hob and catch ! When returned, he rushed in and put out the fire. would never again leave the cooker on if he wasn't there and had learnt it is not safe to play in fire stations!

EQUIPMENT CHECK

How many first aid kits, buckets and spanners can you count in the big picture? Add the number stickers in the boxes.

Answers on page 60.

ODD JUPITER OUT

These Jupiter pictures look the same, but one is different. Can you spot the odd one out?

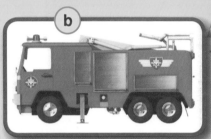

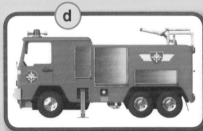

Answer on page 60.

CLOSE-UPS

Can you tell who is in these pictures? Add the matching sticker in the box under each one.

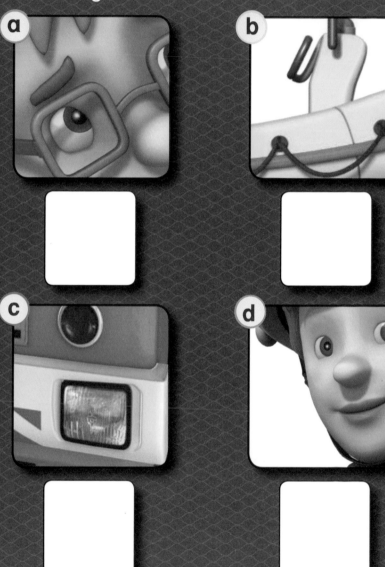

a

b

c

d

Answers on page 61.

COLOUR TIME

Colour in this picture so Sam can put out the fire! You could add some stickers, too.

SAFETY PATTERNS

Add stickers to complete these patterns of fire safety equipment.

1

2

3

Answers on page 61.

NOSY NORMAN

Norman is watching Sam and Penny. These 4 close-ups can all be found in the big picture. Add a tick (✓) in the boxes as you find each one.

a **b** **c** **d**

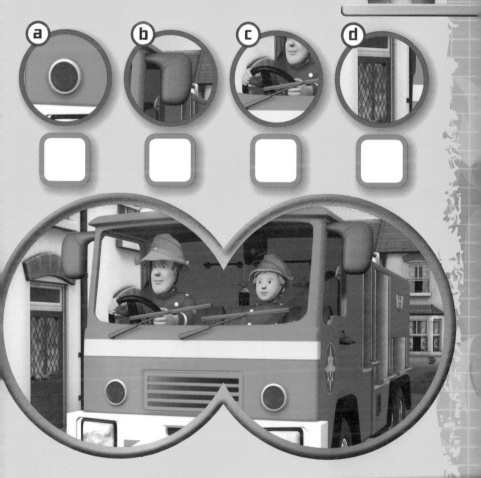

TROUBLE ON THE MOUNTAIN

Which vehicle is first to the mountain rescue? Follow the arrows and put the letters in the boxes to find out

c h l e t i p o r e

Answer on page 6l.

STATION COLOURING

Colour in the Fire Station then add some stickers!

FLOOD'S FLOOD

Mike Flood starts a small repair job at the café, but he's soon in **BIG TROUBLE** ...

One morning, Sam and Elvis see Trevor setting up a mike for the karaoke party.

"I'm singing a duet with Mike tonight," Elvis tells Sam.

"I'm sure you'll be **GREAT!**" Sam replies.

At the café, Mike is repairing the broken cellar door. The handle comes off in his hand!

Mike hears water dripping inside the cellar. "You have a **LEAK!**" he tells Bronwyn.

The fire crew is learning how to rescue people from locked rooms. Officer Steele is shut in a cupboard and pretends to be an old lady who needs help!

"We'll be right with you, Sir, I mean Madam," Sam says.

"Thank you, young man," Officer Steele replies in a little old lady voice.

Mike decides to repair the dripping pipe before he fixes the cellar door. Bronwyn puts a bucket in the doorway to hold the door open while she goes out. Mike tightens the pipe but it **SNAPS** and water gushes into the cellar!

"I should turn the water off at the mains," Mike says to himself. But he picks up the bucket and the door slams shut. Mike and Lion are **TRAPPED**!

When Bronwyn comes back she realises Mike is in **DANGER**, so she calls the fire crew.

The alarm goes off before the crew get Officer Steele out of the cupboard. They try to unlock it, but the door is stuck! **"RESCUE MIKE FIRST,"** Officer Steele tells them.

The crew races to the café. Their priority is to get Mike out of danger.

"STAND BACK," Sam says. "I'll break down the cellar door!"

Mike puts Lion in the bucket and steps back from the door.

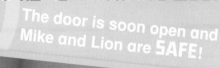

The door is soon open and Mike and Lion are **SAFE**!

Penny turns off the water at the mains and Elvis pumps the water out of the cellar.

Sam hurries back to the fire station to rescue Officer Steele!

That night, everyone goes to the karaoke party.
Soon it's time for Elvis and Mike to sing.

"WOO HOO! COME ON,
MIKE AND ELVIS!" everyone shouts.

"WELL DONE, BOYS," says Officer Steele, accidentally speaking in a little old lady voice!

"AHEM, I MEAN WELL DONE, MEN!" he adds, as everyone laughs!

THE END

ANSWERS

PAGE 26-27

PAGE 28

a – Elvis
b – Trevor
c – Officer Steele
d – Norman

PAGE 29

1

2

3

PAGE 38

Fireman Sam – **5**
Officer Steele – **3**
Jupiter – **6**
Tom Thomas – **2**

PAGE 39

c	j	s	h	o	s	e
t	n	l	n	k	p	r
t	o	r	c	h	s	e
j	f	t	h	p	b	a
w	k	c	n	o	r	x
n	m	f	r	l	b	e
h	e	l	m	e	t	d

PAGE 42

1 first aid kit
3 buckets
4 spanners

PAGE 43

Picture **d** is the odd one out as the ladder is missing from the roof.

PAGE 44

a –

b –

c –

d –

PAGE 48

The helicopter
gets there first.

PAGE 46

1

2

3

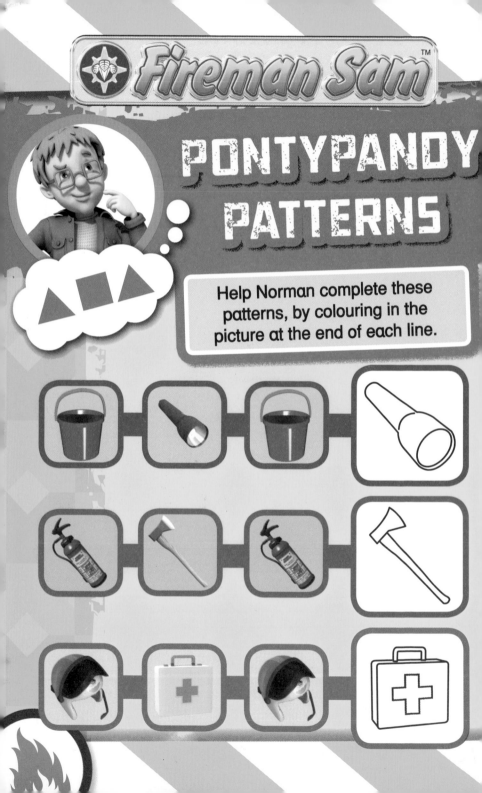